101 Uses
for
Stinging Nettles

Other books by Piers Warren

Non-fiction

How to Store Your Garden Produce

British Native Trees - Their Past and Present Uses

Careers in Wildlife Film-making

Go Wild with Your Camcorder - How to Make Wildlife Films

Fiction

The Hatters Go West!

101 Uses
for
Stinging Nettles

Piers Warren

Published by

Wildeye
United Kingdom

Email: info@wildeye.co.uk
Websites: www.wildeye.co.uk/stinging-nettles
www.wildeye.co.uk/publishing

ISBN (13 digit) 978-0-9541899-9-0
(10 digit) 0-9541899-9-X

Many thanks to Roland Clare for copy-editing.

Contents

Introduction

I expect your first question is 'Are there really that many uses for stinging nettles?' The answer most definitely is *yes* – and more besides, depending on how you categorise them.

Your second question might be 'Why on earth write about the uses of stinging nettles?' Well I have two very good reasons: the first is that from a practical point of view these are uses that you may be able to put to your benefit; the second is that stinging nettles are a good example of the valuable natural resources that surround us, yet are often ignored.

We are becoming aware that disappearing rainforests contain many plants that can be of great use to mankind – in combating disease for example – and let's hope we are realising this before it is too late. But in our own back yards we also have many useful plants, most of which we think of as weeds and destroy. With our increasingly disposable and environment-damaging lifestyles it is important to value the resources that nature has given us.

Everything has its place in nature, and, even if you don't end up enjoying a nettle omelette, or gargling nettle juice to ease your sore throat, I hope you will think of nettles with a little more affection and respect after reading this book. Stinging nettles, like wasps, are often thought of as unnecessary evils of the natural world, but they are vital elements of the web of life. If we look into the past we see that our ancestors indeed made much use of stinging nettles (and many other wild plants too) and most of these uses are just as valid today.

Above all, nettles are extremely good for us. They are packed with vitamins, minerals and fibre, and have many healing properties. Before we start looking at some of the uses, let's have a brief look at the plant itself.

The Botany of Stinging Nettles

There are actually hundreds of species of nettle from all over the world, but for the purposes of this article we are generally talking about the common stinging nettle *Urtica dioica*. It is a very hardy perennial that can be found growing almost anywhere – waste ground, gardens, pasture, hedges, verges and so on.

It can reach seven feet tall and has long, branching, yellowish roots which sprout new plants. The plant has opposite, heart-shaped, finely-toothed leaves which are downy underneath. Both the leaves and the stems are covered with tiny stinging hairs.

In July to September small, greenish-white female flowers appear in clusters at leaf axils; male flowers appear on different plants as groups of diagonally upright strands at the top of the plant. They are wind pollinated and produce small seeds (or nutlets) enclosed in the dried sepals.

The Sting

The millions of minute spines that cover the plant are like hollow glass tubes filled with a cocktail of formic acid, histamine, acetylcholine, seratonin and other chemicals. When they touch our skin the spines are fine enough to penetrate, but they then break off, releasing the venom beneath the surface of the skin. This causes an instant burning sensation and a red rash with the characteristic little bumps.

The name *nettle* comes from the Dutch *netel* – meaning needle – but it is unclear whether this is referring to the stinging needle-like hairs or the fact that cloth was once made from nettle cord and sewn with needles. The genus name *Urtica* comes from the Latin *uro* which means 'burn', and the species name *dioica* means 'two houses' – referring to the fact that the male and female flowers are produced on different plants. The phrase *grasp the nettle* means 'deal with a problem bravely'.

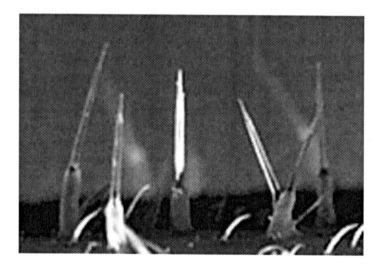

There is a variety of plants that will bring relief from nettle stings when their leaves are rubbed over the affected area, including dock, plantain, marigold, sage, rosemary, mint and the nettle itself (use just the juice not the leaves if using nettles!). Note that it is the juice from these leaves that gives relief – so rub *briskly* to rupture the leaf cells (wear gloves to release nettle juice). Toothpaste also does the trick!

Collecting Nettles

First of all make sure the nettles you are collecting are away from roadsides (to avoid dirt and pollution) and not in areas where they may have been sprayed with chemicals (or have picked up spray drift from an adjacent field). Better would be from the middle of a wood, or ideally from your own nettle patch in your organic wildlife garden.

Identification is not a problem as most of us have learnt from an early age to identify the plant that stings. Although there are a number of *Urtica* species found in Europe and North America they are all similar and can be used for the purposes described in this book. Care needs to be taken in certain other countries, however – for example in New Zealand beware of the fierce tree nettle *Urtica ferox* which not only has a far more painful sting than the common nettle, but can also impair breathing and in some cases has even caused death.

There are various theories about how to handle nettles – 'grasp them firmly and you won't be stung' for example. It also depends on the quality of the skin of the picker – hands with rough hard skin that are used to working outside are less likely to be stung than those with soft indoor skin. But there are some who have got the knack of sting-free picking – or of fewer stings anyway – by being bold. I was told when I was young that if you truly believe you won't be stung you won't be – but it's almost impossible to believe that if you have been stung in the past! Some nettles have a greater concentration of hairs than others and consequently will sting more.

In any case I recommend rolling your shirt sleeves down and wearing a pair of gardening gloves or kitchen gloves when collecting nettles. If you are picking long stems, for the compost heap for example, then make sure you don't whip yourself in the face with the tops. The juicy young shoots for cooking or preparing medications can be pulled off, or cut with secateurs, and collected in old supermarket bags or in a wicker basket. There are people who actually like getting stung and deliberately pick nettles without gloves – some of them describe subsequent improvements to arthritic hands as a result.

Leaves and stems of older plants should not be collected for eating or medicinal uses. As well as being stringy and unpleasant, they can irritate the kidneys possibly owing to a build up of calcium carbonate crystals within the plant's cells.
Roots can be easily collected by pulling up a large nettle plant and cutting the long trailing roots into sections – these can be used in some medicinal preparations or even to plant in your wildlife garden. Alternatively they could be planted in pots in your greenhouse to produce fresh young shoots at times of the year when wild nettles have become unpalatable.

Collecting the seeds for cooking or sowing can be done by cutting the mature stems after the flowers have died down and the seeds have formed. Hang the stems, tied in bundles, to dry and then shake them over large pieces of paper to gather the seeds that fall out. The added advantage of this method is that the dried nettles will no longer sting.

Storing Nettles

Freezing and drying are the two main methods for storing nettles for many of the uses they can be put to. Do this in the spring after collecting the young fresh tips for use later in the year when the plants have become stringy and bitter.

To freeze nettles wash the leaves well, chop and then blanch in boiling water for two minutes. Cool and squeeze out excess water before freezing in plastic bags. The pulp will freeze as a solid lump so fill each bag with only as much nettle as you will need for one meal. To cook from frozen boil for about five minutes.

Alternatively nettles can be dried in a warm, dry place. An airing cupboard may do, but will take a few days; a warm oven (45 – 55°C) will take a few hours. The nettles can be hung in bunches or laid out on a baking sheet. When the leaves are dry, crumble them into glass jars, seal, label and store in a cool, dark place.

If you have collected the seeds as described above they can also be stored in glass jars in a cool, dark place. Whether frozen or dried your nettles will never need to be stored longer than about nine months – for then next year's new shoots should be appearing – and it's always better to use fresh than stored produce.

Nettles in the Garden

To start with we must not overlook the uses the nettle has as a growing plant. It is one of the most important native plants for wildlife in Britain and many other countries, supporting numerous species of insect including some of our most colourful butterflies. It also provides cover for many small animals.

Ideally part of your garden will be left to grow wild as a wildlife patch – and this area should have many nettles which you can introduce, if need be, by planting pieces of nettle root dug up from elsewhere. If you don't have enough room for a wildlife patch you can grow nettles in large pots or tubs – this also stops the plant from taking over via its spreading roots. Place in full sun to attract as many insects as possible.

1. Butterfly and Moth Food

Species that use nettles as a food plant for their caterpillars include:

Comma (*Polygonia c–album*)
Painted Lady (*Vanessa cardui*)
Peacock (*Inachis io*)
Red Admiral (*Vanessa atalanta*)
Small Tortoiseshell (*Aglais urticae*)
Beautiful Golden Y Moth (*Autographa pulchrina*)
Burnished Brass Moth (*Diachrysia chrysitis*)
Green Carpet Moth (*Colostygia pectinataria*)
The Spectacle Moth (*Abrostola triplasia*)

Use nettles to attract these beautiful insects to your garden and you will also benefit from their flower pollinating activities.

2. Pest Control

Ladybirds also use nettles for rearing their larvae – the adults will then move around your garden devouring aphids from your crops. Other natural pest-controllers that use nettles are hover flies, lacewings and parasitic wasps.

3. Bird Food

In early summer birds such as great tits and blue tits will feed on the aphids found on nettles, and in late summer the huge quantity of seed produced provides a food source for many of our seed-eating birds.

4. Compost

Nettles are a great addition to the compost heap – being rich in nitrogen they really get the bacteria going which will break down the rest of the heap. Use layers of cut nettles in between other compostable material.

5. Mulch

Cut up nettles (except the roots) and use as a mulch around plants to keep the soil moist and suppress weed growth. As the nettles rot down they will also supply nitrogen and minerals to the soil below.

6. Liquid Plant Food

Nettles make an excellent general plant food, packed with nitrogen, and also containing magnesium, iron and sulphur.

To make the liquid feed first of all gather some water-tight containers – anything from buckets to barrels depending on what's available and how many nettles you have access to. Harvest nettles (young ones in spring are highest in nutrients, but any will do) and stuff them into the containers – pack them in tight to within six inches of the top. Then pour in water until the nettles are just covered and leave for about two weeks. During this time a sort of fermentation will occur and the liquid will start to froth.

When this has died down just strain off the remaining stems and leaves – you could use a soil-sieve on top of a bucket and just tip the mixture in. And there you have it – a bucket of free, natural, concentrated plant food. Just throw the strained-out solids on the compost heap. To use this liquid, dilute one part to ten parts of water (just do this roughly – straight into a watering can). Then use once every two weeks or so – it's great for hungry vegetables, plants in containers, in the Polytunnel, greenhouse and so on.

7. House Plant Food

This same liquid can be diluted further to be used as a house-plant food. Remember this will be needed only during the growing seasons of spring and summer. In general you can water with the liquid feed once or twice a week depending on how vigorous growth is, watering with rain water (preferably) in between.

8. Insecticide

The liquid produced as described above will also act as an insecticide when sprayed on to other plants under attack from aphids. Alternatively you can make a quicker version of the liquid by simply boiling a large handful of nettles in a pan of water for about half an hour. Strain the liquid, cool and pour into a spray bottle for applying to affected plants.

9. Fungicide

Nettle leaves can be packed around apples, pears etc after you have picked them at the end of autumn to decrease the likelihood of fungus spreading through the fruits. The spray made by the method for a liquid plant food has also been diluted and used as a treatment against mildew.

10. Companion Plant

Nettles make a good companion plant (a plant that benefits its neighbour) as they can help other plants become more resistant to disease, and increase the essential oils in neighbouring plants. Of course they also have the added companion advantages of attracting pollinating bees and aphid-eating ladybirds. Nettles are also said to improve the health of soft fruits, such as blackcurrants, when grown among their bushes, and to reduce the number of fruits eaten by birds. There is the problem of nettles spreading via their roots, however, so in many situations you may want to confine them to large pots among your other plants.

Nettles in the Kitchen

Nettles are packed with vitamin C, a high level of protein, and many necessary minerals including iron. They can be used fresh, or dried and powdered, and simply mixed into any savoury dish, or used in many recipes. Early spring is definitely the best time to pick nettles for eating, when the shoots are only a few inches high. Later in the summer the leaves will turn coarse and taste bitter.

11. As a Vegetable

Young nettle leaves can be cooked like spinach. After removing the stems and washing the leaves, put them in a pan with just the water that clings to the leaves from washing. Cover the pan and boil for about four minutes. Then add a knob of butter, salt and pepper, and cook for a further four minutes while mashing or stirring. They can be served as a side vegetable as they are, or added to other dishes as you would a vegetable like spinach. Alternatively just chop the young leaves and add directly to soups, stews etc.

12. Nettle Soup

To make a simple nettle soup, boil the washed leaves in water for about ten minutes, then strain out the leaves or puree them. You can add whatever you normally add to home-made soups such as onions, herbs, potatoes, carrots, celery etc. To thicken the soup, just add mashed potato.

13. Creamed Nettles

Cook and puree nettles as described above, add cream, chopped chives, crushed garlic and salt and pepper. This can be used as a filling for baked potatoes, for example.

14. Nettle Pie

To make a filling suitable for a vegetarian pie, mix nettles with sliced mushrooms and chopped nuts (in 4:2:1 quantities e.g. 200g nettles, 100g mushrooms, 50g nuts). Fry together for five minutes then add a couple of large spoonfuls of cottage cheese, herbs and seasoning. Mix well before filling a pastry pie-case and baking.

15. Rennet Substitute

The juice of the nettle, or a decoction formed by boiling leaves in a strong solution of salt, will curdle milk, providing the cheese-maker with a good substitute for rennet.

16. Cheese Additive

Tiny bits of nettle leaf can be added to cheese in the same way as with other herbs. These can either be dried leaves, crumbled, or fresh leaves that have been cooked, drained and finely chopped. The nettles can be added as the cheese is formed, or mixed with a soft cheese (e.g. goat's cheese) when ready for eating.

17. Cheese Ripener

Slipcoat (or Slipcote) was a popular cheese a few hundred years ago, sometimes known as *nettle cheese*. It was made in a round only an inch thick so it would ripen quickly – normally it was ready to eat in about ten days. It was made with cow's or ewe's milk. Once the cheese was formed, salted and left for a day it was laid on a bed of nettles, with more nettles on the top which hastened the ripening of the cheese. The nettles were changed once a day until the cheese was ready for eating. Cornish Yarg cheese was also wrapped in nettle leaves while ripening.

18. Salt Substitute

The collected and dried seeds can be ground with a pestle in a mortar to be used as a salt substitute.

19. Nettle Pasta

Similar to spinach pasta and producing a superb green-coloured dough:

Wash 100g of nettle tips, boil for a few minutes then drain and puree with a tablespoon of olive oil. Mix in two beaten eggs and then add this mixture to 500g of strong flour or pasta flour. Mix to form a dough and then knead for a few minutes until the pasta is firm and elastic. Divide the pasta into four lumps, cover in cling film and chill them in the fridge for thirty minutes or more.

When you are ready to cook the pasta, roll out each lump to about 1cm thick and then pass through a pasta machine several times as you would for any other pasta. When you have done this with all the pasta and made the shapes you want it can be boiled for just a couple of minutes before being served with a sauce of your choice. If you don't have a pasta machine simply roll the pasta out thinly and cut into strips or shapes.

20. Pasta Sauce

Chopped leaves (fresh or dry) can be added to many dishes to add flavour and goodness – add them chopped to a tomato pasta sauce for example. You can use a little – as you would with a herb like thyme – or a lot – as you would with a vegetable like spinach. For the complete nettle experience why not pour your nettle pasta sauce over bright green home-made nettle pasta.

21. Nettle Omelette

Nettles can be added to omelettes as you would other herbs, as crumbled dried leaves or fresh leaves that have been cooked and drained and chopped. Similarly they make an unusual addition to quiches as they go well with eggs.

22. Nettle Cake

If you want to try something more adventurous how about nettle cake? This recipe was often used in World War II: first cook a few handfuls of nettles for a few minutes in a little water. Place a layer of breadcrumbs at least half an inch deep in the bottom of a dish and then add the cooked, strained nettles and a layer of fried onions. Add your choice of meat (whatever you have to spare – pork, chicken etc) or pulses (beans or lentils etc). Then add at least half a pint of stock, or the water from boiling the nettles, and finish with a final layer of bacon if desired. Bake this in the oven at 180°C for about half an hour. This can be served on its own as it is, or with gravy.

23. Nettle Pudding

A similar savoury nettle dish – this one Samuel Pepys refers to in his diary on 25 February 1661: saying "*We did eat some Nettle porridge, which was very good.*" It is also referred to as Scottish Nettle Pudding or Nettle Haggis.

To make nettle pudding first take a few handfuls of young nettle tops and wash them. Chop a large leek or onion, and a head of broccoli or a small cabbage, and mix with the nettles along with seasoning and herbs. Place the mixture in a muslin bag, in layers with about 100g of rice in between, and tie tightly. Boil in salted water for about an hour. Serve with gravy or melted butter.

24. Nettles on Toast

Try nettles on toast for a quick snack. Heat a few spoonfuls of pureed nettles with some butter, lemon juice and a little Marmite or Worcestershire sauce. Spread the mixture on to slices of toast, top with a small amount of grated cheese and then grill until it is bubbling on top.

25. Nettle Pizza

Nettles make an interesting and unusual addition to pizzas. They can be added on top of a tomato sauce as dried, crumbled, or finely-chopped fresh leaves, as you would with other herbs, before the cheese is sprinkled over. Alternatively cooked nettles can be used as a topping, as you would with spinach. Try nettle and ricotta pizza for example.

26. Nettle Bread

Simply add a couple of spoons of ground dried or very finely-chopped fresh nettle leaves to the dough mixture before kneading and baking.

27. Nettle Beer

There is some confusion about the difference between nettle beer and nettle wine and I have seen similar recipes called by either name. Nettle beer can still be bought in the Czech Republic and in the north of England where it is brewed with hops. Some recipes suggest replacing half the amount of hops with nettles, or even replacing all of the hops. Of course before the use of hops became widespread in the 17th century many other plants were used to flavour ales and the practice of adding brewing herbs for flavour continued even after hops became popular.

The following recipe is similar to a country wine recipe, but is often called nettle beer: it produces a beverage ready for drinking in a short time.

> **To make nettle beer:** boil 2 kg nettle tips with 4 sliced lemons in 9 litres of water for about 20 minutes. Strain and add 1 kg brown sugar and 25g cream of tartar. When cool add a tablespoon of dried (or brewer's) yeast then pour into demijohns or other vessels which are then fitted with a fermentation lock. Leave the demijohns in a warm place to ferment for three days. Then leave for a couple of days in a cool place before racking (siphoning while leaving solid residues behind) into sterile bottles, which are corked and stored somewhere cool and dark. This drink doesn't keep long and you can start drinking it a week after bottling.

Old recipes often suggest adding handfuls of dandelion and goosegrass and 50g of bruised root ginger before brewing for a refreshing summer drink.

28. Nettle Wine

There are also many recipes called nettle wine – for specific techniques you should consult a wine-making book, but a basic recipe for making nettle wine (which can be stored for months, unlike the quick beverage above) is as follows:

To make nettle wine: bring 4 litres of water to the boil and add about 1kg of nettle tips, the juice and peelings from a lemon, an orange and 2kg of sugar. Stir to dissolve the sugar and allow the mixture to cool. Then add one teaspoon of dried yeast and pour the liquid into demijohns or other fermentation vessels and leave in a warm place. After five days of fermentation strain the liquid into further demijohns and attach airlocks. When the liquid is clear, rack into demijohns and fit airlocks again. Then leave for about three months before racking into sterile bottles, which are corked and stored somewhere cool and dark. You can start to drink this wine straight away once it is bottled.

29. Nettle Tea

To make nettle tea: simply pour boiling water over half-a-dozen freshly-picked and washed leaves in a mug. After 5–10 minutes scoop out the leaves and enjoy the drink. You can also make it with dried nettle leaves or buy organic nettle tea-bags from your health food supplier. Sweeten with honey if required.

Medicinal Nettles

For centuries nettles have been used for their healing properties. Nettles may be used for medicinal purposes in many forms including as a tea, tincture, compress, in ointment or powdered form, depending on the area of use; or they can simply be eaten in the methods already described. They can also be externally applied to treat skin conditions. Don't forget that nettles can be used to treat many of these conditions in your animals as well.

There are many references in ancient herbals to the use of nettles – in fact you end up with the impression that nettles can be used as a treatment for pretty much every ailment known. The following is translated from The Greek Herbal 512 AD:

> *"The Nettle which some call Knide [some Adice, ye Romans Urtica, ye Egyptians Selepsion, ye Dacians Dyn...]. There is a double kind of them, for ye one is wilder, sharper, & blacker in ye leaves but it hath a seed like to Hempseed, but smaller, and ye other is of a thin seed, & not alike sharp. But ye leaves of either of them being smeared on with salt, doe heal things bitten by dogs, & Grangranicall, & malignant, & cancerous, & ye foulness of ulcers, & luxations, tumours, ye Parotidas, ye Pani, Apostumations. But they are laid to ye splenicall with Cerat. And ye leaves being beaten small, & applied with the juice are good for ye fluxes of blood from ye nostrils. They move also ye menstrua being small beaten & applied with Myrrh, & ye new leaves being laid to, do restore ye fallings down of ye matrix. And ye seed being drank with Passum doth incite to conjunction, & doth unstop ye womb, but being licked in with honey it helps ye Orthopneas & Pleursies & Peripneumonies, & fetcheth up ye stuff out of ye Thorax. It is mixed also with septicalls. But ye leaves being sodden together with small shellfish, do mollify ye bellies, dissolve windiness, move ye urine. But being sodden with Ptisana, doth bring up ye stuff from ye Thorax. But ye decoction of ye leaves being drank with a little myrrh, moveth ye menstrua, but ye juice being gargarized doth keep down an inflamed Uvula."*

As already mentioned nettles are a good source of vitamin C, but they can also deliver vitamins A, B1, B2,

E and K. They also contain the trace minerals aluminium, bromine, chromium, cobalt, copper, fluorine, manganese, nickel, silicon and zinc as well as providing beneficial iron, calcium, magnesium and sulphur.

Preparations

You can either make your own nettle preparations or buy them in various forms, such as powders, capsules, tea-bags and pills, from a health food shop, herbalist or over the Internet. Remember, if you are picking your own, to pick only clean young shoots in the spring. In most cases the aerial parts of the nettle are recommended (i.e. leaves, stems, flowers etc) but in some other cases, such as prostrate treatment, preparations from the roots are to be used.

The following terms are often used for preparations:

Infusion / Tea – the ingredients are soaked or steeped in hot or cold water for a period of time before straining the solids out and drinking the liquid. The most common form is to make a tea by steeping washed leaves in boiled water for a few minutes. The longer the leaves are steeped the stronger the infusion – five minutes will produce a refreshing tea, twenty minutes a stronger health tonic.

Decoction – the ingredients are placed in cold water, brought to the boil, and simmered for up to twenty minutes before straining the solids out and drinking the cooled liquid. This is a more suitable method for the roots, which should be chopped before placing in the water.

Infusions and decoctions can be made fresh each time, or you can make a larger quantity and refrigerate for up to three days. If taking the liquid from the fridge, always warm before drinking, to aid digestion.

Juice – an electric juicer or press can be used to extract pure nettle juice. This can be diluted before taking if desired.

Dried – you can dry your own as described in the section *Storing Nettles,* and use them crumbled in foods or direct on to wounds; or buy them freeze-dried in capsule form.

Tincture – this is basically an extraction in alcohol which is particularly suitable for nettle roots. Chop 200g of the roots and add to a jar containing half a litre of strong brandy or vodka. Leave in a dark place for 8–14 days then squeeze out the roots, strain and keep the liquid in a dark bottle. Take one teaspoonful of the tincture two or three times a day.

Ointment – this is to be used externally, for skin conditions for example. For a home-made nettle ointment place half a litre of vegetable oil in a bowl with a cupful of dried nettle leaf and 25g of beeswax. Place the bowl in a pan of hot water and heat for several hours, stirring occasionally. Then strain the liquid into jars where it should set as an ointment as it cools.

<u>**Disclaimer**</u>

Of course it is recommended that, before embarking on any of the treatments below, you discuss your condition with your doctor first. The following is not a guide to treatment, but gives an idea of the many medicinal uses of nettles as a starting point. The author/publishers cannot be held responsible for the affects of any of the remedies described in this book.

30. Arthritis and Rheumatism

Rheumatism – or rheumatoid arthritis – is a form of arthritis that can be described as disease or damage to the joints resulting in pain. Sufferers have found that after being stung by nettles the arthritic pain in their hands subsided – and this was preferable, despite the added pain of the stings themselves (wasp stings are also administered in the same connection).

This treatment may have started in Roman times when the soldiers in cold damp Britain found that stinging themselves with nettles eased their rheumatism. Now there are many people who regularly sting themselves with fresh nettles around affected joints. It is thought that this relief could be caused by the serotonin and histamine in the stings: these are neuro-transmitters that send and receive signals to the brain and act on nerve endings to block the transmission and perception of pain.

31. Gout

This joint inflammation, often in the foot or knee, causes pain which often starts at night and gets worse throughout the next day. This disease is caused by excess uric acid in the blood which deposits in the affected joints. As taking nettles increases the excretion of uric acid from the body they are an effective treatment which has been recommended for some time.

32. Bronchitis

Bronchitis is inflammation of the air passages to the lungs. This can be caused by a viral infection and is certainly worse for smokers. Nettles have anti-viral properties which can help reduce the infection and also have expectorant properties which loosen and reduce coughing by bringing up mucus and expelling it from the chest and throat. To ease bronchitis nettles can be taken in many forms including tea, juice and as seeds. It can be used as a soothing tonic for ex-smokers.

33. Whooping Cough

Whooping cough is a bacterial infection of the respiratory tract. The expectorant and soothing qualities of nettles can ease this as well as all coughs – try drinking a warm nettle tea.

34. Pleurisy

Pleurisy is caused by swelling and irritation of the membrane that surrounds the lungs: it is usually a symptom of another illness. Pleurisy can develop from many things, including bacterial or viral infections of the lungs. Sometimes a cause cannot be found but the problem can still be treated. Symptoms of pleurisy include severe chest pain that starts suddenly. The pain is often strong or stabbing when you take a deep breath. Nettles can help relieve the symptoms, as mentioned by the 17th-century astrologer-physician Nicholas Culpepper:

> *"The roots or leaves, or the juice of them, boiled and made into an electuary with honey and sugar, is a safe and sure medicine to open the passages of the lungs, which is the cause of wheezing and shortness of the breath. It helps to expectorate phlegm and to raise the imposthumed pleurisy."*

35. Hay Fever

Otherwise known as *allergic rhinitis*. Sufferers have been taking nettle preparations for some time to ease their condition thanks to the antihistamine and anti-inflammatory properties of the plant. Many tests have been done showing that nettles do offer symptomatic relief to a significant proportion of people – it is certainly one of the most effective natural remedies for hay fever. They can be taken in many forms including daily drinks of nettle tea, but freeze-dried nettles are said to be the most effective. You can take two 300mg capsules of freeze-dried nettle three times a day, starting a couple of weeks before hay fever season begins.

36. Allergies

An allergic reaction is caused when your body's immune system overreacts when trying to defend you from something it identifies as harmful. Occasionally it is reacting to something completely harmless like nuts. Hay fever is an example of an allergic reaction but there are many others, and allergies in general seem to be on the increase. The release of histamines by your immune system during any allergic attack can be eased by the antihistamine properties of nettles. The result is that the cells in the bodies responsible for releasing histamines are stabilised and reduce less of the chemical. Take as capsules, tinctures or as nettle tea.

37. Asthma

During an asthma attack the muscles of the air tubes in the lung (bronchi) contract in spasms making breathing difficult. This can be caused by an external allergen such as house dust or cat hairs, or occur suddenly with no identifiable cause. The antihistamine properties of nettles have already been described and can be effective against asthma. In fact four hundred years ago British herbalist Nicholas Culpeper claimed that nettle roots or leaves, used in juice or tea, were

> "*safe and sure medicines to open the pipes and passages of the lungs*".

38. Colds

There are so many reasons why nettles should be a top natural remedy for treating common colds. They are packed with vitamin C, can reduce inflammation of the mucous membranes of the nose during a cold, and they have anti-viral and antihistamine properties.

39. Influenza

Unlike a common cold 'flu' will also give you headaches, fevers and exhaustion. Children and old people are more likely to suffer and it can be serious – thousands of people die each year from 'flu'. As well as treating the infection (as described for colds) nettle tonics can be taken regularly to reduce the likelihood of infection should one encounter a 'flu' virus.

40. Sore Throat

Drinking warm nettle tea will ease a sore throat, as well as providing all the weapons for attacking the underlying infection that may have caused the affliction in the first place.

41. Sore Mouth

There can be many reasons for a sore mouth, including ulcers and gum disease: a nettle gargle can be very soothing and help hasten the healing. To make a nettle gargle, boil fresh washed nettles in water for a few minutes, strain out the leaves with a fine sieve or tea strainer, cool and then gargle with the liquid several times a day. Unlike some mouth washes it doesn't matter if you swallow this – in fact it will do you even more good if you do!

42. Scurvy

The high vitamin C content of nettles has made them an effective treatment for scurvy – our ancestors used to eat nettles as soon as they appeared in spring to stave off scurvy after a winter with few fresh greens. This was one of the first attributes of nettles proved by medical tests. Scurvy can cause bleeding gums, loose teeth, sore joints, bleeding under the skin and anaemia. It is not just a disease of the past, however: it is regularly found in young people today who dine on vitamin-poor junk food and shun fresh fruit and vegetables.

43. Neuralgia

This is a pain in nerve pathways caused either by an injury or by a particular disorder. In many cases the cause is not found. It often occurs in the face and can be a result of shingles or a tooth abscess for example. As the serotonin and histamine in the stings of nettles send and receive signals to the brain to act on nerve endings and block the transmission and perception of pain, they have proved an effective relief of neuralgia pain.

44. Sciatica

This is pain or numbness along the sciatic nerve which usually presents itself as lower back pain. It is very common and may have many causes including injury, strains, slipped discs, bad posture and so on. As described for neuralgia, the blocking of pain transmission as a result of taking nettle preparations can lead to soothing of the symptoms.

45. Anaemia

Nettle juice is a good source of iron and can be taken to ease anaemia. The juice can be taken neat or diluted with water or milk. You can make your own juice by pressing washed young nettle tips, or using an electric juicer; or you can buy bottles of ready-prepared organic nettle juice from specialists.

46. Exhaustion

Nettles in the form of seeds, juice or tea have been recommended as a general tonic and pick-me-up. Use when feeling run-down or exhausted, or even as a boost after a long winter.

47. Stress

Similarly a spoonful of nettle seeds or a cup of nettle tea can be soothing in times of stress.

48. Milk Flow

Drinking nettle juice or tea throughout pregnancy and lactation is said to produce enriched breast milk.

49. Pregnancy Tonic

There is a number of additional benefits of drinking nettle infusions (often combined with raspberry leaf) before and throughout pregnancy including:

Strengthening the kidneys. Since the kidneys must cleanse 150 percent of the normal blood supply for most of the pregnancy, nettles' ability to nourish and strengthen them is of major importance.

Increasing fertility in women and men.

Nourishment for mother and foetus.

Easing leg cramps and other spasms.

Note that there are a few references that advise caution when taking nettles while pregnant, so consult your health advisor first.

50. Birth Pain

The high calcium content of nettles, which is readily assimilated, helps diminish muscle pains in the uterus, in the legs and elsewhere both during and after birth. Additionally fresh nettle juice, taken in teaspoon doses, slows bleeding after the birth.

51. Premenstrual Tension

PMT is a complicated syndrome with many different symptoms involving changes in mind, body and emotions leading up to menstruation. It is experienced by 90% of all women at some point in their lives. Many turn to herbal remedies to ease them through this period and nettles are often part of the remedy.

52. Vaginal Yeast Infections

These are very common infections, currently on the increase due to the common use of antibiotics which kill off beneficial bacteria that can normally fight off the yeast infection. Nettles can help fight off these infections and can be taken in numerous ways including bathing – brew some strong nettle tea and pour it into your bath.

53. Blood Pressure

Any preparation made from the leaves, stems or flowers of the nettle will act as a mild diuretic which encourages the body to lose water through urine. As a result nettles have been used as a mild way of relieving high blood pressure.

54. Urinary Tract Conditions

As nettles act as a diuretic they can prove an effective ally in combating infections of the urinary tract. Take nettle tea along with large quantities of water to help flush out your system and speed up recovery from the infection.

55. Kidney Stones

Kidney stones are a build-up of minerals and can be caused by many factors including a poor diet and lack of exercise. The larger the stone, the more pain caused: in severe cases they can cause internal bleeding. Nettles can be taken to reduce this bleeding. Daily drinks of nettle tea have been used by some to prevent the formation of kidney stones in the first place.

56. Poor Circulation

Thrashing oneself with nettles has long been used as an aid to increase blood circulation (also see *96. Keeping Warm*).

57. Haemorrhage

Nettles have often been used to help slow down internal bleeding, especially for uterine haemorrhage. Some herbalists advise that one teaspoon of fresh nettle juice per hour can stop intestinal bleeding. Nettle tea can also be taken to help stop excessive bleeding during menstruation.

58. Cuts and Wounds

As nettles speed up the clotting of blood they are also useful in controlling external bleeding. A compress can be made of bandages or cloth soaked in cooled nettle tea covering the wound, or dried nettle powder can be sprinkled directly on to a wound and pressure applied.

59. Burn Relief

Traumatic injuries such as burns may benefit from the use of nettles owing to their ability to draw excess fluid away from the injury site, which helps to reduce swelling.

60. Depression / Melancholia

The B vitamins in nettles help with depression, and the trace minerals are known to help increase stamina and energy which will improve your general feeling of well-being. You can take nettle capsules as prescribed by your health advisor or eat fresh nettles in a number of recipes. In addition serotonin (5-hydroxytryptamine or 5HTP as it is known and marketed by some health supplement suppliers), which is used increasingly to treat depression, is one of the chemicals found in the stings of nettles – so cheer yourself up with a good stinging!

61. Haemorrhoids

Nettle's mild astringency and general nourishing action tightens and strengthens blood vessels, helps maintain arterial elasticity and improves venous resilience: all this helps to reduce haemorrhoids.

62. Diarrhoea

A decoction of the nettle root is astringent, and is suggested to help relieve diarrhoea and dysentery. Other suggestions involve drinking nettle juice.

63. Fevers

An old superstition existed that a fever could be dispelled by pulling a nettle up by the roots, while reciting the name of the sick person and also the names of his or her parents. But in addition to this there are many records of nettles being taken, as juice or tea, as a general tonic to reduce fever and lower temperature.

64. Digestion

Sluggish digestion can be aided by the addition of nettles to soups or by drinking nettle tea before a meal.

65. Prostate

The roots of nettles have become popular for treating the discomforts of an enlarged prostate gland (known as BPH – benign prostatic hyperplasia). Early symptoms of BPH, including night-time urination and residual urine, can be relieved by taking a root preparation. Doing this may also inhibit the hormonal changes that lead to BPH in the first place. Nettle root contains numerous biologically active chemicals that may influence the function of the prostate, interact with sex hormones, slow the growth of prostate cells, fight prostate cancer, and reduce inflammation. Studies treating men with BPH using nettle roots have found significant reductions in prostate size, night-time urination, urination frequency and improved urine flow and residual urine. Frequently, nettle is included with other herbals such as pygeum and saw palmetto in prostate formulas.

Nettle is available as a powder made from the dried root, or in various oral dose forms such as extracts. Extracts are concentrated liquid preparations usually made by soaking the chopped or mashed nettle roots in a liquid such as alcohol, and then straining out the solid parts. Although dosing for nettle root varies, a common recommendation for BPH is 240 mg of nettle-root extract per day.

A tea may be prepared by soaking about one teaspoon of the powdered root in a small cup of boiling water for five to ten minutes. The resulting tea should be strained before drinking it. No more than three cups of nettle root tea should be taken in a day.

66. Weight Loss

A novel treatment for diabetes was reported by an overweight sufferer from that disease in the daily press of April, 1926. Apparently he fasted for two days, then followed a diet of young nettles and drank a nettle brew: this reduced his weight by six stone in three days, vastly improving his diabetic condition. Of course the two days' fast will result in weight loss, and eating young nettles before a fast and drinking nettle tea during it will give you a boost of vitamins and minerals to help your energy levels throughout the fast. I wouldn't expect to lose six stone in three days, however!

67. Blood Sugar / Hypoglycaemia

In addition to the above situation nettle may also contain substances that reduce blood sugar levels, and it has been in used in the past as a treatment for hypoglycaemia. Therefore it should be used cautiously by people already taking hypoglycaemic drugs (i.e. those that lower blood glucose levels) such as insulin.

68. Acne

Nettles may help bind up some of the testosterone and other hormones that may be responsible for the onset of acne. They can be taken as a tea and/or by adding young nettle leaves to the diet. They may equally be taken in capsule form.

69. Eczema

Nettles are recommended by herbalists in cases of childhood eczema (an inflammatory skin disorder) and are beneficial in treating all the varieties of this condition, especially in nervous eczema. Tea or tincture may be taken three times a day. Nettles will combine well with figwort and burdock in the treatment of eczema. Alternatively nettle ointment may be applied directly to the affected area.

Cold nettle tea can also be used as a general skin-conditioner and cleanser.

70. Insect Bites / Bee Stings

Applying juice from the stinging nettle to the skin may relieve itching, burning and pain from insect bites or stings. It can also be applied as an ointment or drunk as tea.

71. Sting Relief

One of the best reliefs from the pain of nettle stings is, surprisingly, juice from the nettle itself. Rub a handful of fresh leaves between gloved hands to release some juice and then spread over the affected area.

72. Dog Bite

There are several references to nettles being used to treat dog bites or after attack from a 'mad dog'. Nettle leaves were mixed with salt and applied to the wound as a poultice.

73. Worms

Nettle beer has been taken as a treatment to get rid of worms of the stomach and intestines. Boiling nettle roots and drinking the liquid has also been used as a de-wormer.

74. Head Lice

There is a number of commercially-available shampoos containing nettle extracts for the treatment of head lice.

75. Dandruff Treatment

Nettles have also long been used as a hair tonic.

To make nettle dandruff treatment: simmer a handful of young nettles in a pint or two of water for two hours, strain and bottle when cold. Saturate the scalp well with the lotion every other night to help prevent dandruff.

76. Hair Shampoo/Conditioner

Nettle shampoo leaves the hair soft and glossy.

To make nettle shampoo: add four teaspoons of dried nettle leaf to half a litre of water and let it soak overnight. Then strain the liquid and add 150g of liquid soap (castile soap) and half a teaspoon of almond oil. You can also add up to fifty drops of your favourite essential oil – lavender is a good addition, for example. Shake the mixture well in a bottle and it is ready to use as you would a normal shampoo.

To make nettle hair conditioner: mix a spoonful of vinegar with two spoonfuls of nettle juice. Massage this into the scalp after washing with shampoo as you would with a normal conditioner, leave for five minutes or so then rinse out.

77. Hair Restorer

For stimulating hair growth (and preventing hair-loss) the old herbalists recommended combing the hair daily with expressed nettle juice. A stimulating hair tincture was made by steeping equal quantities of nettle leaves and chopped onions in alcohol for a few days.

There is a herb called pygeum which blocks an enzyme (5-alpha-reductase) which converts testosterone to dihydrotestosterone, which itself is now thought to cause age onset baldness in men. As nettle is known to enhance the effects of pygeum the two are often combined in modern treatments.

Nettles and Animals

78. Livestock Fodder

Most livestock will not eat fresh nettles, although some goats do; but many will eat dried (or wilted) nettles – alone or incorporated into hay. This is very good for animals kept on the smallholding or farm and is said to increase milk production of cows and goats.

79. Horse Tonic

In Germany dried nettle is mixed with feed for thin horses suffering digestive troubles and to cure racehorses of colds. Horse dealers mixed nettle seed with oats and other feeds to give the animals a sleek coat (and therefore make old specimens more attractive to potential buyers). English horse-dealers were said to feed a mixture of nettle-seed and corn to their animals to make them lively.

80. Poultry Food

Poultry will benefit from nettle leaves boiled up with their mash, or bits of dried leaves mixed in their food. In fact, especially with chickens, this diet is said to increase their egg-laying season. It has also been credited with preventing the disease coccidiosis in chicks.

81. Bull Stimulus

English farmers' wives used to 'encourage' prize bulls during the mating season by beating and stinging them with nettles. This is not recommended for readers of a timid or nervous disposition.

82. Budgie Improver

Budgies have been fed on wilted nettles to improve their condition. In fact small pieces of nettle leaf can be fed to any pet bird – but first pour boiling water over the leaves to neutralise the stings.

83. Pet Food

Dried nettle leaves can be fed to rabbits. Some will be fussy and refuse it, but it is an excellent food for those that like it.

84. Beehive Protection

It is said that nettles grown around the entrance to beehives will protect the bees from predation from frogs.

Nettle Fibre

Nettles produce long and strong fibres to support their long stems. The fibre is very similar to that of hemp or flax, and it was used for the same purposes, from making cloth of the finest texture down to the coarsest, such as sailcloth, sacking, cordage etc. A common method for extracting the fibres was to soak the stems in water for some time to allow bacteria to digest the unwanted tissues, leaving the fibres behind. This process is called *retting*.

85. Nettle Cloth

Nettle is a useful alternative to other natural fibres such as hemp, linen and cotton, and its use is experiencing a renaissance. Today companies in Germany and Switzerland are investigating the commercial production of nettle cloth.

Nettlecloth was manufactured in Scandinavia and Scotland until the nineteenth century, and it was for a long while called *Scotch cloth* in Britain. The Scots in particular used the cloth to make sheets and table cloths.

86. Nettle Clothes

In Hans Christian Andersen's fairy-tale of *The Princess and the Eleven Swans*, the coats she wove for them were made of nettles. Nettle fibres have been used to make army clothing – in the First World War, when they ran out of cotton, Germans collected huge quantities of nettles which were subsequently woven into cloth to make their uniforms. Apparently 40 kg of nettles were required to produce one shirt.

A tropical member of the nettle family is currently used in the production of a silky fabric known as *ramie*, which is currently available in some Italian fashion houses.

87. Nettle Cord

Nettle cord can be put to a number of uses, for example as fishing line.

To make nettle cord: pick a large nettle, strip off the leaves by pulling the stem through a gloved hand and squashing it flat. Split the stem to open it and scrape out the inner pith. Then separate the stem into four strands and plait these together to make an amazingly strong cord. It can be used straight away, or dried and re-soaked which will make it even tougher.

To make a finer cord suitable for weaving, take a number of nettle stems, split them into strips and hang them up to dry. After a few days pull the fibres away from the central pith. They can be combed to clean and separate them. Soak these fibres to soften them and twist a few together (traditionally done on the thigh): add more along the length and keep twisting until you have the length required. To make a thicker, stronger cord twist larger bunches of fibres together and then twist or plait to make a two- or three-ply cord.

---

88. Fishing Nets

Drag nets for fishing were made from nettle fibre in Britain in late mediaeval times. Different sized pieces of wood were kept as measures to make nets of different gauges. Fine nets were said to be almost invisible in water.

89. Nettle Weaving

The cord can be woven to make baskets, mats, bags and rugs as well as to produce softer cloth for clothing.

90. Nettle Jewellery

The cord can also be woven to make bracelets and necklaces. Try using home-grown nettle fibre to make friendship bracelets as presents. You could even dye the threads different shades of yellow and green using nettle dyes (see later) before weaving them together.

91. Nettle Paper

The fibre can even be made into paper – in France, in particular, large quantities of nettles were collected for paper-making. The fine nettle fibres were cut into short lengths (about 2cm) and boiled and soaked to clean, soften and separate before laying in paper-making frames and drying.

Miscellaneous Uses

92. Waterproofing

Nettle juice, if rubbed liberally into small seams in leaky wooden tubs or barrels, coagulates and makes them watertight.

93. Insect Repellent

Although many insects feed solely on the nettle plant, flies have a distaste for it, and a fresh bunch hung up will keep a larder free from them.

94. Dye

A greenish-yellow dye can be made from the leaves and stems of nettles – it colours wool a grey-green and silk a soft cream colour. Alternatively a yellow dye can be made from the roots. During World War II, on order of the County Herb Committees, tons and tons of nettles were gathered and laid out on cricket pitches and sports fields to dry. It was all very hush-hush: no-one was told why it was being done. It turned out that the juice was extracted to dye camouflaged material for the fighting troops.

In Russia the green nettle dye is used for colouring woollen clothing. The yellow dye produced by boiling the roots with alum was widely used in country districts to dye yarn, and is used by Russian peasants to stain eggs yellow on Maundy Thursday.

Nettles have also been used to give a green colour to paints, varnishes and enamels. Commercially the chlorophyll is extracted to give a green colouring-agent for foods and medicines.

In the BBC TV series *The Good Life* Tom and Barbara Good made presents of sweaters, dyed green with nettles, to their neighbours the Ledbetters (showing a comic side to the use of nettles).

> **To make nettle dye:** first gather and chop either the leaves or the roots depending on whether you want to make green or yellow dye. Then place in a large pan with twice as much water as nettle, bring to the boil and simmer for an hour. Strain the liquid and then soak the fabric or yarn to be dyed – the longer you soak it (up to a day) the deeper the colour. Note that it is a good idea to soak the fabric in a colour fixative before dyeing, to make the colour set. To do this simmer the fabric in a mixture of four parts water to one part vinegar. Rinse several times before putting the fabric in the nettle dye. Remember after dyeing to wash the fabrics separately in cool water until the dye remains fast.

95. Burning Oil

The Egyptians used to crush nettle seeds to produce a burning oil which they used in lamps.

96. Keeping Warm

In the first century, when the Romans invaded Britain, their soldiers beat themselves with bunches of nettles to keep themselves warm and get the blood flowing. I'm sure it worked! To make matters worse they also used the Roman Nettle (*Urtica pilulifera*) which they introduced to Britain and which has a more ferocious sting. They also carried the plant into battle to give themselves courage.

Native Americans in the north-west used to sting themselves with nettles to keep awake on long canoe voyages.

97. Stinging Nettle Day

There is a number of special days associated with nettles. On May Day in Liskeard, Cornwall, the local people celebrated *Stinging Nettle Day*. One of the activities involved eating a nettle leaf rolled up in a dock leaf – a practice supposed to keep you safe for the next year. On 2nd May in Cromer, Norfolk and in South Devon, *Sting Nettle Day* was celebrated with various games including boys with handfuls of nettles chasing the girls!

98. Nettle Celebrations

There is an increasing number of activities celebrating nettles throughout Britain and other countries – most of these occur during a week in May known as Be Nice to Nettles Week. Activities change from year to year but here are a few examples from recent years:

"WeedStock" *Staining, Nr. Blackpool Lancs*
Stalls, plays, games and even a mini-opera on all of God's weeds!

"Super Stingers" *Jarrow, Tyne & Wear*
Find out all about nettles on a fun trail, discover what lurks among the nettles in a mini-beast hunt, have a go at using nettles to dye cloth and try some nettle soup, tea and cheese.

"Marvellous Nettles" *Tameside*
Celebrate National Nettle Week by finding out some of the many useful things that nettles can do.

"Nature Bites" *Gateshead*
Are nettles really nasty or are they actually a wonderful weed? Come along and make your own mind up by tickling your taste buds with nettle soup, tea and cheese.

"Grasp The Nettle" *Stour Valley Local Nature Reserve, Bournemouth, Dorset*
A celebration of the nettle. Join the Rangers at the Stour Valley LNR to find out about the natural history of the nettle, its conservation value and its culinary and medicinal uses. The afternoon will consist of an introductory slide-show and a site visit, followed by a chance to cook up some recipes.

"Butterflies & Nettles" *Bushmead Estate, Luton*
A guided walk on butterfly habitats.

"Nettlemania" *Blackpool Stanley Park*
Eat nettles, drink nettles, ride nettle boats on the famous lake. Live music on the stage as well as Nettle

Bingo and *Hands off my Nettle*, a play put on by the local primary school. Kids learn the value of nettles without getting stung.

"Naughty but Nice Nettles" *Swindon*
Considered a troublesome weed with a loathsome sting, the humble nettle gets a lot of bad press. Come along to this drop-in event, discover the nicer side of nettles, their importance to wildlife, join in arts and crafts with 'Artsite' and try some nettle tea in our kelly kettle kitchen!

"Festival of Nettles" *The Scottish Crannog Centre*
Special range of exhibits, hands-on crafts, textiles, and foods celebrating the multi-talented nettle plant and Scottish Biodiversity Week. From string to soup, free fact-sheets and recipes, this extended week offers something for everyone.

"Be Nice to Nettles" *Loch Ness*
Good plant or bad plant? Nettles are perhaps one of our best-known plants. This walk marvels at the brilliant design of nettles and their uses by animals and by us. Get ready to try some nettle soup!

"The Big Nettle Day" *West Sussex*
Find out the truth about nettles! Nettles have a fascinating array of uses from paper and string-making to cooking and dyeing, and are hugely beneficial to wildlife, particularly insects. Nettles are also steeped in folklore and can be usefully grown in any garden.

Further information about events in future years can be found at the website www.nettles.org.uk.

99. Nettle-Eating Competitions

Competitions based on eating the greatest amount of nettles in a certain period of time are popular at a few country fêtes.

The Annual World Nettle-Eating Championship is held at The Bottle Inn, Marshwood in Dorset. Here the contestants have an hour to eat as many nettles as they can without being sick (measured by length of bare stems left after the leaves have been eaten). In 2005, in front of more than 600 spectators, the men's champion Ed Brooks managed 48 feet of nettles and the ladies' joint champions Jo Carter and Liz Gray both managed 26 feet. The world record, however, is 74 feet, held jointly by Simon Sleigh (2004) and Simon Slater (2000). The event was originally the World's Longest Nettle Competition (which drew an amazing 16-foot nettle) but it now attracts nettle-eating entrants from all over the world.

Gloves are not allowed, nor are mouth-numbing drugs, but washing the nettles down with beer is encouraged. The favoured technique is to fold the leaf, push it into the side of the mouth, crunch and swallow, keeping the mouth as wet as possible (hence the beer).

100. Magical Uses

It is said that you can carry nettle in a sachet to remove a curse. Sprinkle nettle around the house to keep evil out, or throw it on to a fire to keep danger away. Wearing nettle is supposed to keep negativity away.

101. Erotic Uses

Urtication is the name given to the practice of using stinging nettles to stimulate the skin for therapeutic reasons or for pleasure during spanking sessions and other such pastimes. It was popular in Victorian times when English mistresses used to beat their masters with nettles to – er – encourage them!

And most city-folk think it's just a weed ...

Further Resources

Be Nice to Nettles Week – find out what you could do during Nettle Week – and the rest of the year for that matter. See what's happening near you or register your own activity: www.nettles.org.uk

Country Smallholding is a practical monthly magazine, for smallholders new and old and anyone with an interest in keeping livestock, growing, organics, the environment, self-sufficiency, and everything related to small scale farming and the Good Life, both in the country and in town. For more information see www.countrysmallholding.com or contact the editor on 01392 888481

Organic Gardening Magazine is the UK's only monthly gardening magazine which is entirely organic. It offers practical, hands-on advice on every aspect of the garden, in-depth growing guides, the latest research and the liveliest opinions: don't garden without it! For more information see www.organicgardeningmagazine.co.uk or tel: 01643 707339

Kitchen Garden Magazine is the UK's leading specialist monthly magazine for growers of fruit and vegetables. A team of specialist writers, including Bob Flowerdew, Toby Buckland, Sue Stickland and Andrew Tokely all expert kitchen gardeners write on all aspects of growing fruit and vegetables in the garden or on the allotment. For more information see www.kitchengarden.co.uk or contact the editor on 01507 529396

Permaculture Magazine is full of practical articles about how to combat climate change and live a greener lifestyle. Covers subjects such as organic gardening, eco-building, renewable energy and ecovillage living. Full of inspiring personal stories. George Monbiot says it is "*an indispensable guide to reclaiming your life.*" Quarterly. For more information see www.permaculture.co.uk or contact info@permaculture.co.uk or tel: 01730 823 311

The **Centre for Alternative Technology** (CAT) is concerned with the search for globally sustainable, whole and ecologically sound technologies and ways of life. They offer solutions to some of the most serious challenges facing our planet and the human race, such as climate change, pollution and the waste of precious resources. Leading by example, they aim to show that living more sustainably is not only easy to attain but can provide a better quality of life. Their Visitor Centre in Wales is open seven days a week. Interactive displays show global issues such as energy generation and transport, and practical, everyday solutions for everyone. For more information see www.cat.org.uk. They also have an online mail order shop with an extensive range of books and products ethically chosen to help you live a more environmentally friendly, sustainable lifestyle – see www.cat.org.uk/shopping

Garden Organic is the working name of the Henry Doubleday Research Association (HDRA). A registered charity, and Europe's largest organic membership organisation. They are dedicated to researching and promoting organic gardening, farming and food. For more information see www.gardenorganic.org.uk

The **Community Composting Network** (CCN) is the national network providing help support and representation to community groups and social enterprises that are in some way involved in the sustainable management of organic waste resources. For more information see www.communitycompost.org or contact info@communitycompost.org or tel: 0114 2580483

eco-logic books publishes and sells mail order books and other products that provide practical solutions to environmental problems, featuring: self sufficiency, biodynamic gardening, eco-villages, crafts, community orchards, chickens in your garden, permaculture, sensible building, useful skills, weird ecothings, alternative energy, living lightly, ponds, sheds, organic gardening, compost and poo. For more information see www.eco-logicbooks.com or contact info@eco-logicbooks.com or tel: 01225 484472

How to Store Your Garden Produce
by Piers Warren published by Green Books

"Every serious gardener should have a copy." — Organic Gardening magazine

"Entertaining and very practical. A great gift for any gardener." — Centre for Alternative Technology

"Practical, useful, good recipes and wonderful illustrations" — éco-logic books

"A veritable Tardis of tips on how to preserve the harvest glut. A perfect present." — The Organic Way magazine

How to Store Your Garden Produce by organic smallholder Piers Warren shows how to store and preserve your garden produce, enabling you to eat home-grown goodness all year round. The easy to use reference section enables you to quickly look up applicable storage and preservation techniques for the majority of plant produce grown commonly in gardens and allotments.

The techniques include
• freezing • clamping • hanging • drying • bottling
• pickling • fermenting

**Available from Green Books Tel: 01803 863260
www.greenbooks.co.uk**

British Native Trees - Their Past and Present Uses

by Piers Warren published by Wildeye

This unique book explores the past and present uses of products (wood, bark, fruit, sap etc) of the 35 species of British native trees.

With sections:

- A genus by genus break down of past and present uses of British native tree products

- A guide to **Coppicing**

- The history and practice of **Charcoal Production**

- **Firewood** - including an exploration of the environmental issues involved in burning wood in the home, sources of firewood, which wood to burn, seasoning and storing firewood, kindling and a foolproof guide to building the **one-match-fire**!

For example - find answers to the following questions:

1. Which tree saps can be used to make wine?

2. Which was the best wood for making longbows?

3. Oil from the bark of which tree is an effective insect repellent?

4. Which tree's bark contains chemical compounds that can selectively kill human cancer cells with no side effects?

5. What is a faggot?

6. What do bodgers do?

7. Which berry was used as a coffee substitute?

8. What wood is the panelling in the House of Commons made of?

9. Which tree's wood has the right acoustic qualities for making electric guitars?

10. Which tree's wood made charcoal taken to cure flatulence?

...and many more fascinating facts!

Available from Wildeye www.wildeye.co.uk/trees

Lightning Source UK Ltd.
Milton Keynes UK
UKOW01f0616030317
295805UK00001B/39/P